For free work sheets and ac
for this book, please em

sisters@holyassumptionmonastery.com

For a whimsical look at how to prepare and how NOT to prepare for Pascha, check out

Pascha at the Duck Pond

and check out the other books of the 3-Day Pascha series!

Great and Holy Friday

Great and Holy Saturday

The Three-Day Pascha
All 3 volumes in one!

Pascha, the Feast of Feasts

from *The Three-Day Pascha*: Orthodox Christian Easter Stories for Children

ISBN-13 978-1946991089

Published by Holy Assumption Monastery
1519 Washington St.
Calistoga, CA 94515

Phone: (707) 942-6244
Website: http://holyassumptionmonastery.com
Email: sisters@holyassumptionmonastery.com

THE THREE-DAY PASCHA SERIES:
Orthodox Christian Easter Stories for Children

Journey with your children through the Three-Day Pascha - the great high point of the story of God's saving love for fallen man and creation. Pascha (the traditional Orthodox name for Easter) is the "Passover" (Pesach) of Christ - and of us through Him - from death to life. So, Great and Holy Friday, Great and Holy Saturday, and the Day of Resurrection are a seamless whole. To think of one without the other two is to misunderstand it.

PASCHA is the Day of Resurrection, the day of sheer joy, and the core of the Christian life. Because Christ is risen, we can be healed of our diseases of body and soul and share in God's life because Christ has shared fully in OUR life.

A final note - This series often refers to the Virgin Mary as the Theotokos, which means "the birthgiver of God." This title has been used since at least the third century in order to guard the truth that Mary's Son is not only fully human, but fully God.

Pascha, the Feast of Feasts

from *The Three-Day Pascha: Orthodox Christian Easter Stories for Children*

by Mother Melania

With illustrations by Bonnie Gillis

HOLY ASSUMPTION MONASTERY
Calistoga, California

The angel cried to the Lady Full of Grace:

Rejoice, O Pure Virgin!

Again I say: Rejoice! Thy Son is risen from

His three days in the tomb!

With Himself He has raised all the dead!

Rejoice, all you people!

Shine! Shine! O New Jerusalem!

The Glory of the Lord has shone on thee!

Exalt now and be glad, O Zion!

Be radiant, O Pure Theotokos,

in the Resurrection of thy Son!

Pascha, the Feast of Feasts

(Pascha is known in the West as "Easter")

Christ is risen from the dead,
trampling down death by death,
and upon those in the tombs bestowing life!

– *Paschal Troparion*

Be glad today! Be glad! Rejoice!

With all creation, lift your voice,

For Christ has died, but lives again –

Restoring Life to fallen men.

Pure Virgin Mother, weep no more.

Thy Son has shattered Hades' doors

For He has gained the victory

O'er death and sets its captives free.

MP
ΘΥ

O Mary Magdalene, rejoice
To see Christ's face and hear His voice!
Then, to the Lord's apostles bring
The news of Christ our Risen King!

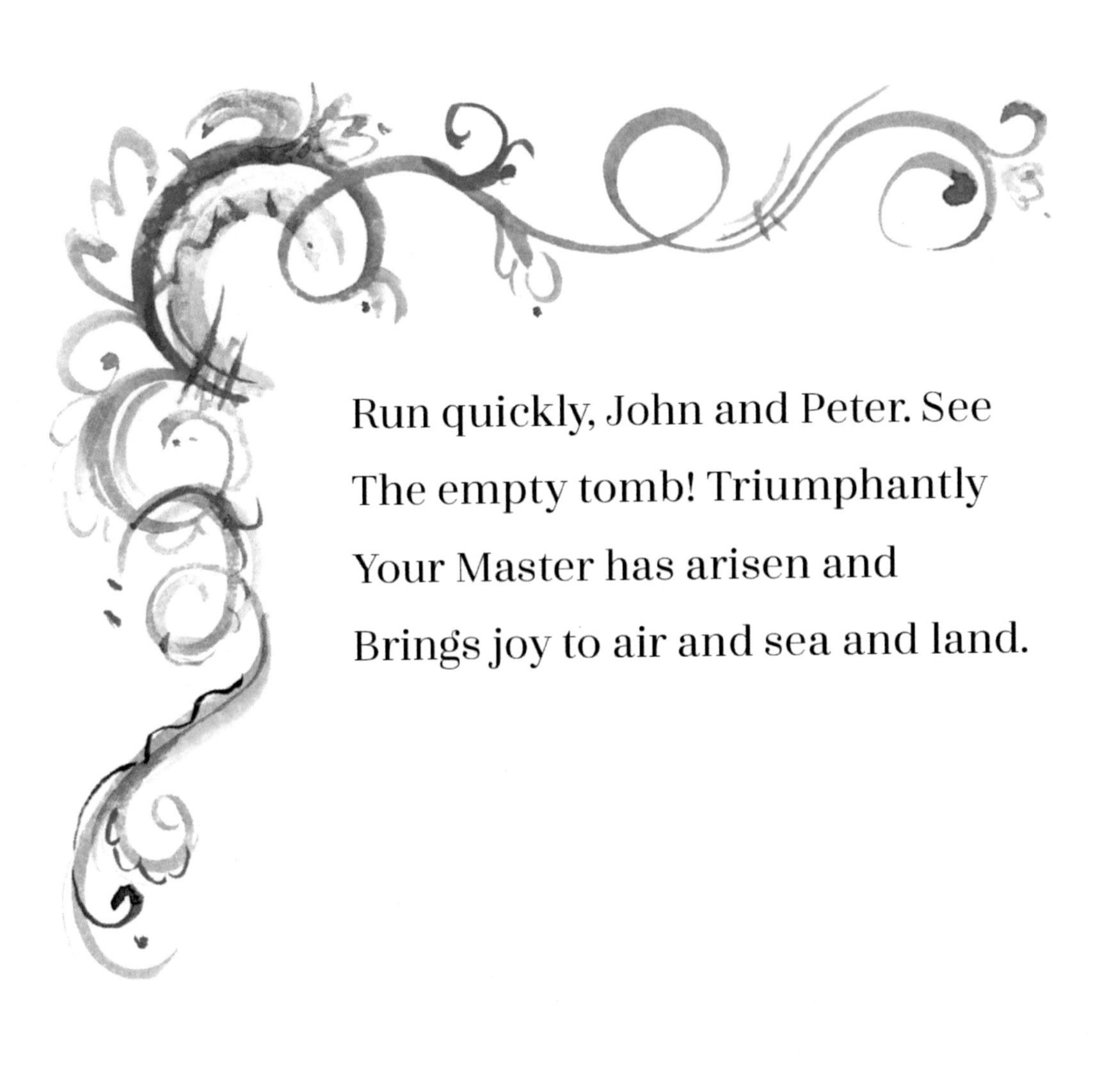

Run quickly, John and Peter. See
The empty tomb! Triumphantly
Your Master has arisen and
Brings joy to air and sea and land.

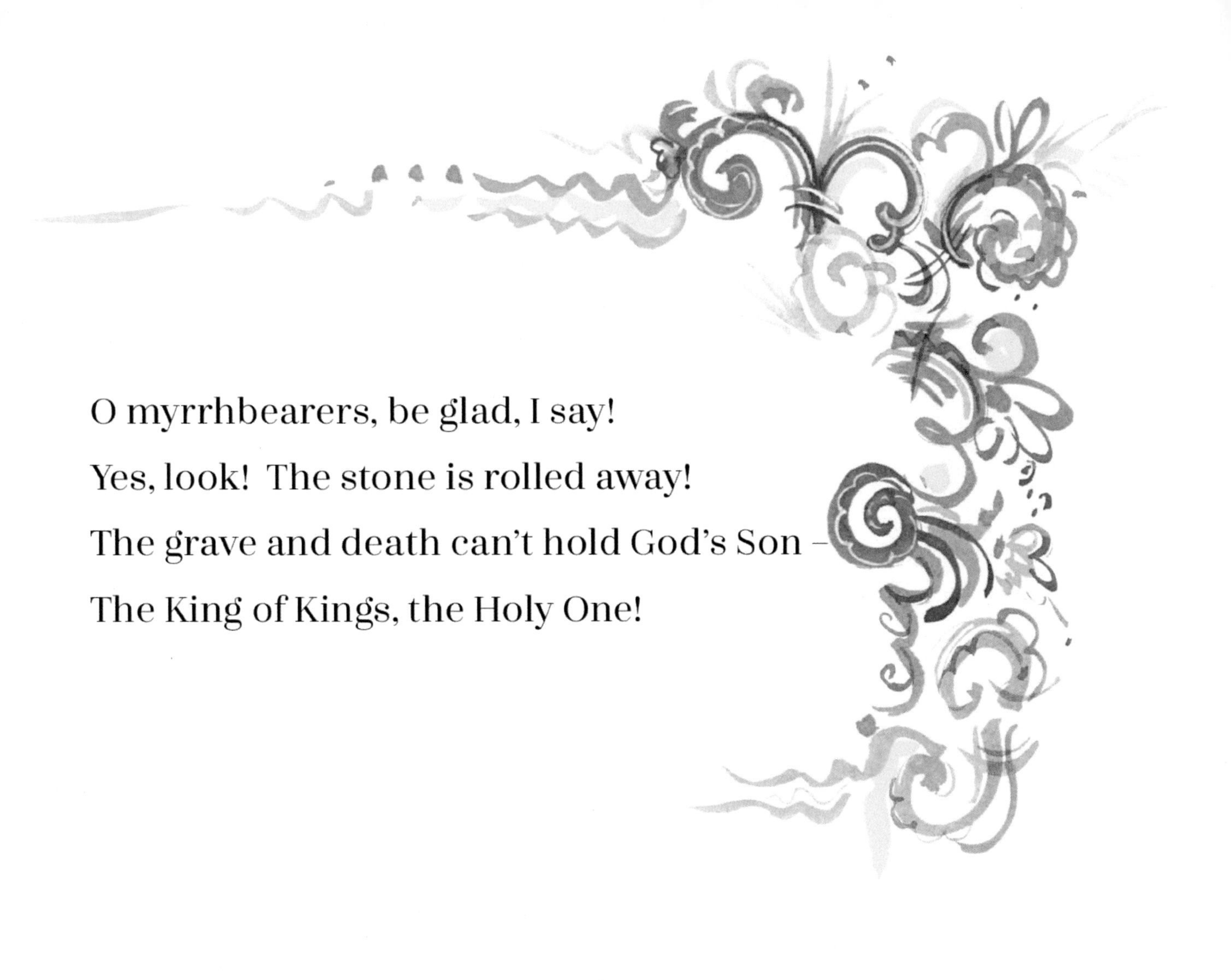

O myrrhbearers, be glad, I say!

Yes, look! The stone is rolled away!

The grave and death can't hold God's Son –

The King of Kings, the Holy One!

Ye dead, rise up now from the tomb
For Christ has scattered death's dark gloom.
With His divine, eternal Light,
He drives away sin's fearsome night.

O Adam, Father of us all,

And Eve our Mother – Christ now calls

You back to paradise where you

Once walked and where His Voice you knew.

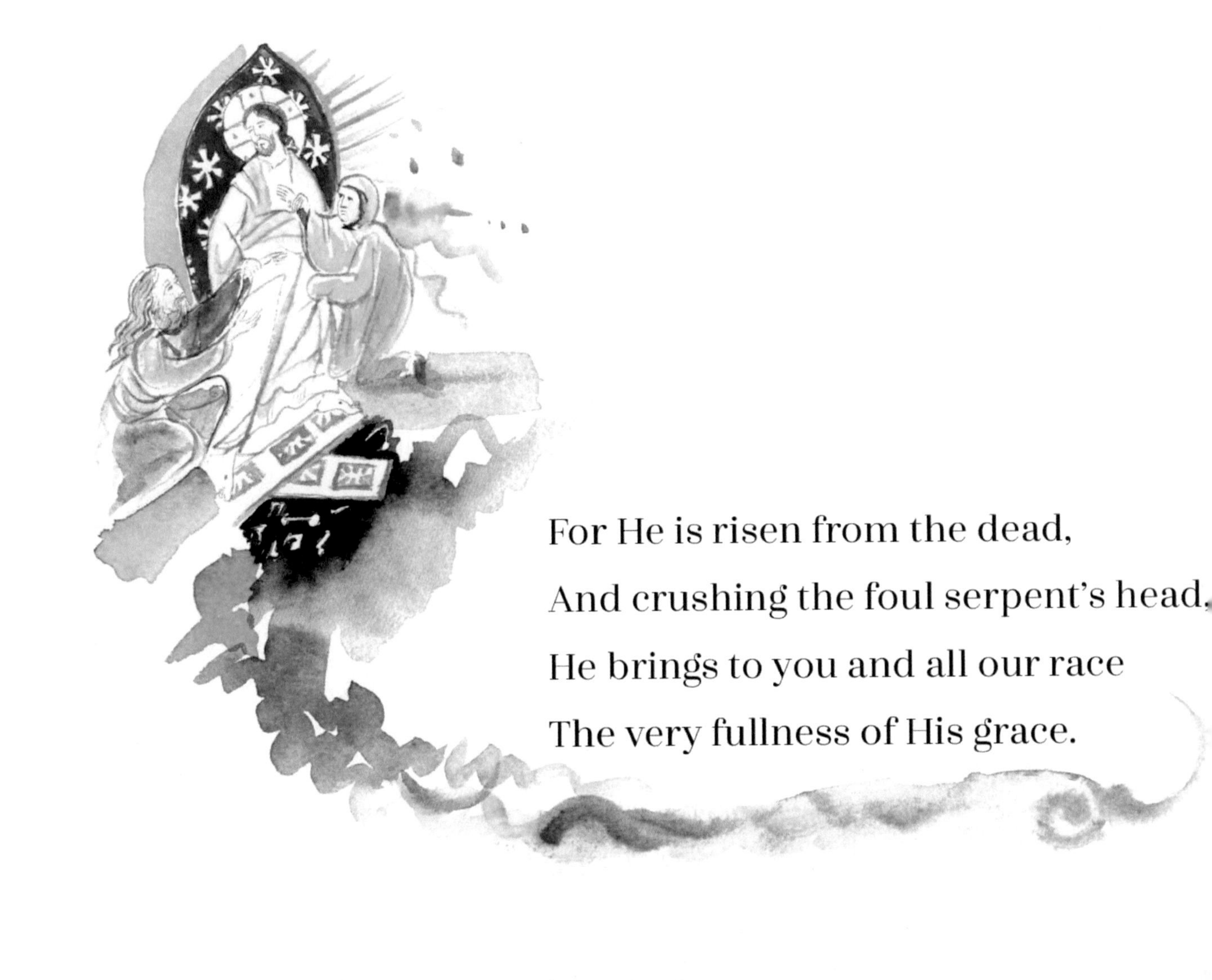

For He is risen from the dead,
And crushing the foul serpent's head,
He brings to you and all our race
The very fullness of His grace.

Ye Christians, worship Him Who lives
Forever, and with joy forgive
Your enemies – remembering
The Resurrection of our King.

O all creation, sing to Him
For Whom the Sun in grief grew dim
For through His death and rising, He
Restores you to true purity.

Be glad, be glad! Lift up your hearts!

For Christ is risen and imparts

God's Life to man, and through man pours

That Life on all things – evermore!

Christ is risen! **Truly, He is risen!**

Please check out Mother Melania's other series.

Capers and Harry
from

the Fearless & Friends series

The Three Holy Youths in the Furnace
from

Old Testament Stories for Children

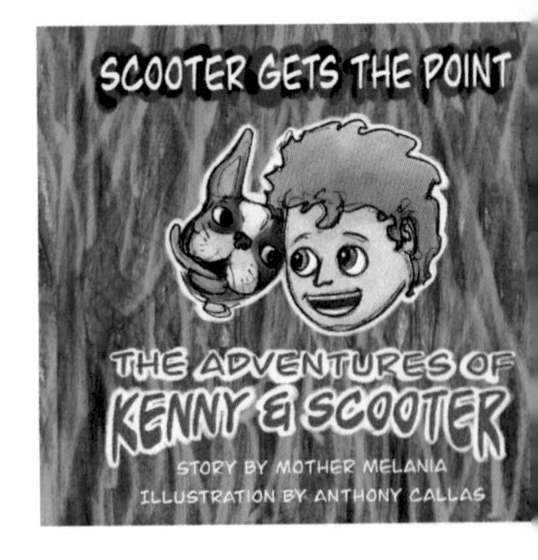

Scooter Gets the Point
from

The Adventures o
Kenny & Scooter

Would you please leave a review on this book's Amazon page?

Your feedback helps us to improve!

Thanks so much, and God bless you!

ABOUT THE AUTHOR AND ILLUSTRATOR

Mother Melania is the abbess of Holy Assumpti
Monastery in Calistoga, California. She has
enjoyed working with children all of her life. In
addition to The Three-Day Pascha series, she h
written several other series of children's books,
focusing on Scriptural stories and Great Feasts
the Church Feasts, and celebrating virtue.

Bonnie Gillis is an iconographer and illustrator
She lives in Langley, British Columbia, Canada
where her husband, Father Michael, is pastor o
Holy Nativity Orthodox Church.

Made in United States
Orlando, FL
01 February 2023